MY FAMILY

My special memories of our family

Alicat

This book was filled in by

_____

_____

When _____

Where _____

For my _____

_____

_____

With all my love,

(Signature)

Contents

Cultivate Your Family Tree!

Most of us can remember our grandparents — and can relate at least a few stories about them, their lives and the kind of world they grew up in. But when we try to recall anecdotes about our great-grandparents, we're likely to hit a brick wall. Many of us don't even know their names! And that's a shame, because these immediate ancestors are part of who we are. To our parents, they were probably familiar figures, and — as their direct descendants — we might even take after them.

Fill in this book and you'll be forging the first link in a chain encompassing your family's history — past and future. By providing invaluable information about yourself and your spouse, your parents and your grandparents, you'll be offering your family a priceless gift of knowledge. This volume, when you've completed it, will enable your children, grandchildren and great-grandchildren the ability to reach much further back into the family tree than you or I could hope to do.

Future members of your family might be interested to learn that they've inherited something, such as their hazel eyes or curly hair, from a distant forebear — perhaps even from you yourself! Or they could find that their musical talent runs in the family, going back to a great-great-grandparent about whom they'd know nothing, if it weren't for this unique family record.

Dates and places are important to note, but remember that it's often the little things that will fascinate the contemporary reader: your grandmother's love of fine china or your grandfather's passion for amateur astronomy. So don't hesitate to flesh out your pen-portraits of your parents and grandparents with personal anecdotes and descriptions. These are the ingredients that bring people, places and times to life.

Two world wars have touched most people, directly or indirectly, in at least two of the generations to be included in this record. Here is the chance to document wartime experiences, which might otherwise be lost forever. There is also space for information about subsequent wars.

You'll probably be able to complete most pages of this book off the top of your head. But there may be a few gaps in the family narrative, particularly when you delve further back in time. In many families there's at least one person who has researched the family tree. But if you're not lucky enough to have an obliging family historian, you can seek help from the numerous genealogical societies' websites listed on the last page.

Here's your chance to write your own family history — and to create a cherished "future heirloom" at the same time. Why not make your family proud?

This volume is a companion to *My Story: Things I want you to know and remember about me*, which not only gives you the chance to describe your own life in more depth but also deals with practical issues. Once you've filled in both books, you can rest assured that you've done everything possible to help your children and grandchildren fully understand their rich heritage.

Children with the same family, the same blood,
with the same first associations and habits,
have some means of enjoyment within their power,
which no subsequent connections can supply.

Jane Austen (1775–1817) *Mansfield Park*

Wife's Family Tree

_____
Wife's maternal grandfather

_____
Wife's paternal grandfather

_____
Wife's maternal grandmother

_____
Wife's paternal grandmother

_____
Wife's mother

_____
Wife's father

_____
Wife

_____
Our children

Husband's Family Tree

_____
Husband's maternal grandfather

_____
Husband's paternal grandfather

_____
Husband's maternal grandmother

_____
Husband's paternal grandmother

_____
Husband's mother

_____
Husband's father

_____
Husband

_____
Our children

Wife and Her Siblings

Wife's full name _____

Maiden name _____ Nickname _____

Date of birth _____ Time of birth _____

Birthplace _____

Height _____ Build _____

Coloring _____ Color of eyes _____

If born overseas, when she came to this country _____

Reason for coming to this country _____

_____

Wife's siblings (in order of birth)

Full name _____

Date of birth _____ Time of birth _____

Birthplace _____

Full name _____

Date of birth _____ Time of birth _____

Birthplace _____

Full name _____

Date of birth _____ Time of birth _____

Birthplace _____

Full name _____

Date of birth _____ Time of birth _____

Birthplace _____

ATTACH PHOTOGRAPHS
OF WIFE AND HER SIBLINGS HERE

Wife's Parents and Grandparents

Wife's mother's given names _____

Maiden name _____

Wife's maternal grandmother's given names _____

_____ Maiden name _____

Wife's maternal grandfather's full name _____

_____

Wife's mother's siblings _____

_____

_____

_____

_____

_____

Wife's father's name _____

Wife's paternal grandmother's given names _____

_____ Maiden name _____

Wife's paternal grandfather's full name _____

_____

Wife's father's siblings _____

_____

_____

_____

_____

_____

Wife's Great-Grandparents

Maternal grandmother's parents

Great-grandmother's name _____

Great-grandfather's name _____

_____

Maternal grandfather's parents

Great-grandmother's name _____

Great-grandfather's name _____

_____

Paternal grandmother's parents

Great-grandmother's name _____

Great-grandfather's name _____

_____

Paternal grandfather's parents

Great-grandmother's name _____

Great-grandfather's name _____

_____

Husband and His Siblings

Full name _____

Nickname _____

Date of birth _____ Time of birth _____

Birthplace _____

Height _____ Build _____

Coloring _____ Color of eyes _____

If born overseas, when he came to this country _____

Reason for coming to this country _____

_____

Husband's siblings (in order of birth)

Full name _____

Date of birth _____ Time of birth _____

Birthplace _____

Full name _____

Date of birth _____ Time of birth _____

Birthplace _____

Full name _____

Date of birth _____ Time of birth _____

Birthplace _____

Full name _____

Date of birth _____ Time of birth _____

Birthplace _____

My Photographs

ATTACH PHOTOGRAPHS
OF HUSBAND AND HIS SIBLINGS HERE

Husband's Parents and Grandparents

Husband's mother's given names _____

Maiden name _____

Husband's maternal grandmother's given names _____

_____ Maiden name _____

Husband's maternal grandfather's full name _____

_____

Husband's mother's siblings _____

_____

_____

_____

_____

Husband's father's name _____

Husband's paternal grandmother's given names _____

_____ Maiden name _____

Husband's paternal grandfather's full name _____

_____

Husband's father's siblings _____

_____

_____

_____

_____

Husband's Great-Grandparents

Maternal grandmother's parents

Great-grandmother's name _____

Great-grandfather's name _____

_____

Maternal grandfather's parents

Great-grandmother's name _____

Great-grandfather's name _____

_____

Paternal grandmother's parents

Great-grandmother's name _____

Great-grandfather's name _____

_____

Paternal grandfather's parents

Great-grandmother's name _____

Great-grandfather's name _____

_____

Maternal Grandmother

Wife's mother

Full name _____

Maiden name _____ Nickname _____

Date of birth _____ Time of birth _____

Birthplace _____

Height _____ Build _____

Coloring _____ Color of eyes _____

If born overseas, when she came to this country _____

Who accompanied her _____

Reason for coming to this country _____

_____

_____

Order in the family (*first, second, etc.*) _____

Where she grew up _____

Her schools _____

_____

Her age when she left school _____

Further education/training _____

_____

Degrees/diplomas, etc. _____

_____

_____

Her occupation _____

_____

Organizations she worked for _____

_____

_____

Special interests/talents _____

_____

_____

War experiences/awards _____

_____

_____

_____

Memories/anecdotes _____

_____

_____

_____

Maternal Grandfather

Wife's father

Full name _____

Nickname _____

Date of birth _____ Time of birth _____

Birthplace _____

Height _____ Build _____

Coloring _____ Color of eyes _____

If born overseas, when he came to this country _____

Who accompanied him _____

Reason for coming to this country _____

_____

_____

Order in the family (*first, second, etc.*) _____

Where he grew up _____

His schools _____

_____

His age when he left school _____

Further education/training _____

_____

Degrees/diplomas, etc. _____

_____

_____

His occupation _____

_____

Organizations he worked for _____

_____

_____

Special interests/talents _____

_____

_____

War experiences/awards _____

_____

_____

_____

Memories/anecdotes _____

_____

_____

_____

Wife's Parents' Marriage

How they met _____

_____

Date of marriage _____ Where it took place _____

_____

The bride wore _____

_____

The bridegroom wore _____

Their reception was held at _____

_____

Guests included _____

_____

Where they spent their honeymoon _____

_____

Where they lived when they returned _____

_____

Addresses of their later family homes _____

_____

_____

_____

_____

_____

They were married for (*number of years*) _____

ATTACH PHOTOGRAPHS OF
MATERNAL GRANDPARENTS HERE

Paternal Grandmother

Husband's mother

Full name _____

Maiden name _____ Nickname _____

Date of birth _____ Time of birth _____

Birthplace _____

Height _____ Build _____

Coloring _____ Color of eyes _____

If born overseas, when she came to this country _____

Who accompanied her _____

Reason for coming to this country _____

_____

_____

Order in the family (*first, second, etc.*) _____

Where she grew up _____

Her schools _____

_____

Her age when she left school _____

Further education/training _____

_____

Degrees/diplomas, etc. _____

_____

_____

Her occupation _____

_____

Organizations she worked for _____

_____

_____

Special interests/talents _____

_____

_____

War experiences/awards _____

_____

_____

_____

Memories/anecdotes _____

_____

_____

_____

Paternal Grandfather

Husband's father

Full name _____

Nickname _____

Date of birth _____ Time of birth _____

Birthplace _____

Height _____ Build _____

Coloring _____ Color of eyes _____

If born overseas, when he came to this country _____

Who accompanied him _____

Reason for coming to this country _____

_____

_____

Order in the family (*first, second, etc.*) _____

Where he grew up _____

His schools _____

_____

His age when he left school _____

Further education/training _____

_____

Degrees/diplomas, etc. _____

_____

_____

His occupation _____

_____

Organizations he worked for _____

_____

_____

Special interests/talents _____

_____

_____

War experiences/awards _____

_____

_____

_____

Memories/anecdotes _____

_____

_____

_____

Husband's Parents' Marriage

How they met _____

_____

Date of marriage _____ Where it took place _____

_____

The bride wore _____

_____

The bridegroom wore _____

Their reception was held at _____

_____

Guests included _____

_____

Where they spent their honeymoon _____

_____

Where they lived when they returned _____

_____

Addresses of their later family homes _____

_____

_____

_____

_____

_____

They were married for (*number of years*) _____

My Photographs

ATTACH PHOTOGRAPHS OF
PATERNAL GRANDPARENTS HERE

Wife's Childhood

Names of elementary schools _____

_____

Favorite playground games _____

_____

Best friends in elementary school _____

Pocket money _____ What she spent it on _____

Household jobs _____

Names of junior high schools _____

_____

Favorite subjects _____

Favorite teachers _____

Best friends in junior high school _____

Favorite books _____

_____

Favorite music _____

_____

Favorite television shows, movies and actors _____

_____

_____

Favorite sports _____

_____

Place of worship attended _____

ATTACH PHOTOGRAPH HERE

Childhood holidays _____

_____

_____

Makes and models of family cars _____

_____

_____

_____

Childhood pets _____

_____

_____

_____

Special childhood memories _____

_____

_____

_____

_____

Wife's Adult Years

Higher education _____

_____

Diplomas/degrees _____

_____

Her first job was with (*name of organization*) _____

Her position _____

Weekly salary _____ Price of a newspaper _____

Special friends _____

_____

Favorite sports teams _____

_____

Favorite music _____

_____

Favorite books _____

_____

_____

Favorite television shows _____

_____

_____

Favorite movies and actors _____

_____

_____

Other jobs (*names of organizations and positions held*) _____

_____

_____

_____

_____

Special interests/pastimes _____

_____

_____

_____

Special memories/achievements _____

_____

_____

_____

_____

_____

War service/awards _____

_____

_____

_____

Husband's Childhood

Names of elementary schools _____

_____

Favorite playground games _____

_____

Best friends in elementary school _____

Pocket money _____ What he spent it on _____

Household jobs _____

Names of junior high schools _____

_____

Favorite subjects _____

Favorite teachers _____

Best friends in junior high school _____

Favorite books _____

_____

Favorite music _____

_____

Favorite television shows, movies and actors _____

_____

_____

Favorite sports _____

_____

Place of worship attended _____

Childhood holidays _____

_____

_____

Makes and models of family cars _____

_____

_____

_____

Childhood pets _____

_____

_____

_____

Special childhood memories _____

_____

_____

_____

_____

Husband's Adult Years

Higher education _____

_____

Diplomas/degrees _____

_____

His first job was with (*name of organization*) _____

His position _____

Weekly salary _____ Price of a newspaper _____

Special friends _____

_____

Favorite sports teams _____

_____

_____

Favorite music _____

_____

Favorite books _____

_____

Favorite television shows _____

_____

_____

Favorite movies and actors _____

_____

_____

Other jobs (*names of organizations and positions held*) _____

_____

_____

_____

_____

Special interests/pastimes _____

_____

_____

_____

_____

Special memories/achievements _____

_____

_____

_____

_____

_____

_____

War service/awards _____

_____

_____

_____

_____

Our Courtship

How we met _____

_____

_____

Our first date _____

_____

What we liked about each other _____

_____

We became engaged on (*date*) _____

How we celebrated our engagement _____

_____

Description of the ring _____ What it cost _____

"Our song" _____

We were engaged for (*length of time*) _____

How much money we saved up before marriage _____

Special memories of our courtship _____

_____

_____

_____

_____

_____

_____

_____

ATTACH PHOTOGRAPHS
OF WIFE AND HUSBAND
WHEN YOUNG

Our Wedding

Date of wedding _____ Where it took place _____

Priest/celebrant _____

Description of bride's outfit _____

_____

_____

Description of bridegroom's attire _____

_____

Names of bride's attendants _____

_____

_____

Best man and groomsmen _____

_____

_____

Music played _____

People who attended the service included _____

_____

_____

_____

_____

_____

_____

_____

My Photographs

ATTACH WEDDING
PHOTOGRAPHS HERE

Our Reception

It was held at (*time*) _____ Venue _____

_____

Speeches were made by _____

_____

Food and wine served _____

_____

Decorations _____

_____

Music played _____

_____

Special customs _____

_____

Bride's "going-away" outfit _____

_____

Wedding gifts we still have _____

_____

_____

Special memories of the day _____

_____

_____

_____

_____

Our Honeymoon

Where we went _____

_____

How we got there _____

How long we were away _____

Special memories of our wedding day and honeymoon _____

_____

_____

_____

_____

_____

_____

_____

_____

_____

_____

_____

_____

_____

_____

_____

Our Early Years of Marriage

Where we lived when we returned from our honeymoon _____

_____

Where we worked _____

_____

Our first dinner guests _____

_____

What we served them _____

_____

Our favorite recipe book _____

_____

Our first "good" piece of furniture _____

_____

Our proudest possessions _____

_____

Our favorite radio/television shows _____

_____

Our favorite records/CDs _____

_____

Memories/anecdotes _____

_____

_____

_____

Our Children

Full name _____

Date of birth _____ Time of birth _____

Birthplace _____

Coloring _____ Color of eyes _____

Who he/she takes after _____

Personality and temperament _____

_____

Full name _____

Date of birth _____ Time of birth _____

Birthplace _____

Coloring _____ Color of eyes _____

Who he/she takes after _____

Personality and temperament _____

_____

Full name _____

Date of birth _____ Time of birth _____

Birthplace _____

Coloring _____ Color of eyes _____

Who he/she takes after _____

Personality and temperament _____

_____

Note: If you have more than three children, simply photocopy this page and add into journal.

Family Album

ATTACH PHOTOGRAPHS OF YOU
AND YOUR CHILDREN HERE

Family Album

ATTACH PHOTOGRAPHS OF YOU
AND YOUR CHILDREN HERE

Our Family Homes

We brought our first baby home to (*address*) _____

_____

Description of apartment/house _____

We lived there for (*length of time*) _____

Memories _____

_____

_____

Address of our second home _____

_____

Description _____

How long we lived there _____

Memories _____

_____

_____

Addresses and memories of our other family homes

_____

_____

_____

_____

_____

_____

Our Family Vacations

Our first holiday with our children _____

_____

How we got there _____

Favorite holiday destinations _____

_____

_____

_____

Things we liked to do _____

_____

Special vacations _____

_____

_____

_____

_____

Anecdotes and memories _____

_____

_____

_____

_____

_____

Our Family Pets

Name _____ Type of pet _____

Endearing qualities _____

Not-so-lovable qualities _____

How long we had him/her _____

Anecdotes _____

_____

Name _____ Type of pet _____

Endearing qualities _____

Not-so-lovable qualities _____

How long we had him/her _____

Anecdotes _____

_____

Name _____ Type of pet _____

Endearing qualities _____

Not-so-lovable qualities _____

How long we had him/her _____

Anecdotes _____

_____

Other special pets _____

_____

_____

_____

My Photographs

ATTACH PHOTOGRAPHS
OF YOUR PETS HERE

Changes We've Seen

*Anyone who was born in the first half of the 20th century has seen
enormous changes to daily life: the advent of the supermarket,
the end of milk and bread deliveries (by horse and cart)
and the introduction of television and computers, to name a few.*

How we traveled to school _____

_____

Where we bought groceries, etc. _____

_____

How children entertained themselves after school and on weekends _____

_____

_____

Neighbors we were friendly with _____

_____

A typical Sunday _____

_____

Evening entertainments _____

_____

Other daily home deliveries _____

The number of newspapers in our town/city _____

How often we traveled by plane _____

How often we went to restaurants or bought take-out meals _____

A typical home-cooked meal _____

_____

_____

Wife's special anecdotes about life when she was young

_____

_____

_____

_____

_____

_____

_____

_____

Husband's special anecdotes about life when he was young

_____

_____

_____

_____

_____

_____

_____

_____

Wife's Cousins

Children of her mother's siblings

_____

_____

_____

_____

_____

_____

_____

Children of her father's siblings

_____

_____

_____

_____

_____

_____

_____

Husband's Cousins

Children of his mother's siblings

_____

_____

_____

_____

_____

_____

_____

Children of his father's siblings

_____

_____

_____

_____

_____

_____

_____

_____

Our Nieces and Nephews

Wife's nieces and nephews

_____

_____

_____

_____

_____

_____

_____

_____

Husband's nieces and nephews

_____

_____

_____

_____

_____

_____

_____

_____

Other Special Family Members

*Most of us are particularly close to certain members of our extended family –
perhaps an aunt who understood children or a second-cousin of our own age.
Or perhaps you'd like to write about a stepparent or step-sister or -brother.
This page is for these special members of your family.*

More About Wife's Great-Grandparents

Maternal grandmother's parents

Great-grandmother's name _____

Date of birth _____ Birthplace _____

Where she lived as an adult _____

If she came here from another country, date of arrival _____

Coloring _____ Build _____

Occupation _____

Special talents/interests _____

_____

_____

_____

Great-grandfather's name _____

Date of birth _____ Birthplace _____

Where he lived as an adult _____

If he came here from another country, date of arrival _____

Coloring _____ Build _____

Occupation _____

Special talents/interests _____

_____

_____

_____

Maternal grandfather's parents

Great-grandmother's name _____

Date of birth _____ Birthplace _____

Where she lived as an adult _____

If she came here from another country, date of arrival _____

Coloring _____ Build _____

Occupation _____

Special talents/interests _____

_____

_____

_____

Great-grandfather's name _____

Date of birth _____ Birthplace _____

Where he lived as an adult _____

If he came here from another country, date of arrival _____

Coloring _____ Build _____

Occupation _____

Special talents/interests _____

_____

_____

_____

_____

Paternal grandmother's parents

Great-grandmother's name _____

Date of birth _____ Birthplace _____

Where she lived as an adult _____

If she came here from another country, date of arrival _____

Coloring _____ Build _____

Occupation _____

Special talents/interests _____

_____

_____

_____

Great-grandfather's name _____

Date of birth _____ Birthplace _____

Where he lived as an adult _____

If he came here from another country, date of arrival _____

Coloring _____ Build _____

Occupation _____

Special talents/interests _____

_____

_____

_____

_____

Paternal grandfather's parents

Great-grandmother's name _____

Date of birth _____ Birthplace _____

Where she lived as an adult _____

If she came here from another country, date of arrival _____

Coloring _____ Build _____

Occupation _____

Special talents/interests _____

_____

_____

_____

Great-grandfather's name _____

Date of birth _____ Birthplace _____

Where he lived as an adult _____

If he came here from another country, date of arrival _____

Coloring _____ Build _____

Occupation _____

Special talents/interests _____

_____

_____

_____

_____

Family Heirlooms

You may have a sampler stitched by your great-grandmother,
a portrait of a distant ancestor, or furniture and ornaments
that your parents brought out from their homeland.
You may even have a diary written by a great-grandparent.
Even if these things are owned by someone else
in the family, it would be worth recording their existence here.

Description of item _____

When it was made _____ Where it came from _____

Special family history attached to it _____

_____

_____

Who owns it now _____

Description of item _____

When it was made _____ Where it came from _____

Special family history attached to it _____

_____

_____

Who owns it now _____

Description of item _____

When it was made _____ Where it came from _____

Special family history attached to it _____

_____

_____

Who owns it now _____

Description of item _____

When it was made _____ Where it came from _____

Special family history attached to it _____

_____

_____

_____

Who owns it now _____

Description of item _____

When it was made _____ Where it came from _____

Special family history attached to it _____

_____

_____

_____

Who owns it now _____

Description of item _____

When it was made _____ Where it came from _____

Special family history attached to it _____

_____

_____

_____

Who owns it now _____

Wife's Wartime Memories

*This page has been included for women who lived through World War II.
Even those who were babies or children during the war may have memories
of wartime civilian life, post-war rationing, etc. Or perhaps you were involved
in the Korean War, Vietnam or a later military engagement.
Your recollections will be of great interest to later generations.*

Husband's Wartime Memories

This page has been included for men who lived through World War II.
Even those who were babies or children during the war may have memories
of wartime civilian life, post-war rationing, etc. Or perhaps you were involved
in the Korean War, Vietnam or a later military engagement.
Your recollections will be of great interest to later generations.

Genealogical Websites

The internet is a powerful tool to help you fill the gaps that might appear when completing this book.

There are many family history websites that search an ever growing collection of official records. Look for birth, death, marriage or divorce certificates of your ancestors. Census material is now available online. Browse historic maps to see the places where your ancestors and relatives lived. Your search is only limited by your imagination.

Whether you call it family history, genealogy, or ancestry research, your research can be not only fun but rewarding. To start, try these search engines, and fine tune your search by adding the country you are interested in.

www.ancestry.com.

www.myheritage.com

www.familysearch.org

When a society or a civilization perishes,
one condition can always be found.
They forgot where they came from.

Carle Sandburg

Alicat

16 Sandilands Street
South Melbourne VIC 3205 Australia
Email: publishing@alicat.com.au
www.alicat.com.au

Publisher: Ali Horgan
Editor: Maggie Pinkney
Production: Angie McKenzie

First published 2013

Printed in China 5 4 3 2 1

ISBN 978 1 74340 278 8